STUDY AID ASSIGNMENTS TO ACCOMPANY

Introduction to Western Concert Music

ARMAND AMBROSINI

MICHAEL LEE

The University of Oklahoma

KENDALL/HUNT PUBLISHING COMPANY
4050 Westmark Drive   Dubuque, Iowa 52002

Contents

Preface

This study aid is specifically designed to accompany Armand Ambrosini and Michael Lee's *Introduction to Western Concert Music*. It is provided to assist the student after all assigned reading has been completed in preparing for class lectures, meaningful discussions, and exams. Through a variety of formats such as matching, vocabulary, fill in the blank questions, questions for discussion and essay, listening assignments, and so forth, the student engages in an activity of synthesizing material and conceptual principles discussed in the text.

This guide is divided into fifteen parts, each relating directly to the designated chapter of the textbook on which this text is based, with three Concert Report Forms at the back that may be used in conjunction with listening assignments. The course the reader is taking will most likely not have enough time to cover all the material in these sections, so the student may check off only those topics that are assigned. After responding to questions, the students should always check their answers against the assigned reading in the textbook. Since an answer key for questions is not provided in this manual, the instructor may take advantage of the perforated pages and use portions of this guide for classroom quizzes, tests, or for home assignments. Questions for Discussion or Essay in this study aid, and at the end of each historical chapter of the textbook, are intended to stimulate thought and interaction both inside and outside of class, given that some are explorative and others argumentative. Consequently, the student should always feel prepared to engage the various subjects addressed.

As listening is the basic activity that leads to understanding music, student attendance at live performances is essential, for despite the particularly high quality of a recording and playback system, there are clearly major differences between live and recorded performances. A live performance at the very least encourages active participation, as it is a social phenomenon inherently interactive. Herewith, Concert Report Forms provided in this study aid offer the interested student the opportunity to respond in writing about various concert experiences, and to begin the process of using a precise musical vocabulary for relating in-depth observations.

Most recognize arts education as an integral part of the university environment, an important role not only for art's sake, but also for its contribution to the consummate knowledge and wisdom of any individual. Hence this textbook and study aid do not serve to promote connoisseurship (how valuable is this piece of music), rather, they are intended to model a devised plan for engaging music as a social practice toward fostering better understanding. Clearly, it is not the only way to study music, but the authors believe it is a fruitful way to assist interested students seeking a more sophisticated way of engaging this vital field of human endeavor.

CHAPTER 1
Introduction to Western Concert Music and Society

𝄢 Fill in the Blank

1. Plato, one of the West's most persuasive philosophers, argued that gymnastics should form fully one half of a student's education, as it perfected the body, and the other half should be _____, as it perfected the mind.

2. Plato's vision for music education was twofold; he advocated learning to play an instrument or sing in addition to advocating _____ engagement with music.

3. Eduard Hanslick taught the first music _____ class in Vienna in the late 1800s to inform and to encourage audiences to value what he valued; it is a term that flows from a connoisseur's sensibility.

4. Far more than half of the human beings who have ever lived on this planet were alive during some part of the _____ century.

5. Western concert music is often called _____ music.

𝄢 Questions for Discussion or Essay

I. Plato's two-part curriculum of music and gymnastics gave way to the study of the trivium and the quadrivium during the Middle Ages. Music, considered an essential and basic mental discipline in the West, also formed part of the quadrivium, along with arithmetic, geometry, and astronomy. As educational systems have long ago abandoned the trivium and quadrivium as the foundation for the curriculum, what part, if any, did music play in your education thus far? If your musical background is substantial, do you believe that you were advantaged in any way by your education? How so? If your education has lacked a solid musical basis, do you believe that you have been disadvantaged in any way by your school curriculum? How so?

II. Plato felt that music was at once a pleasure that could keep the attention of the student, while at the same time music was a useful illustration of mathematical ratios and formulas in motion. He hoped music's power to illustrate physical properties and potentials would reveal to the student the pleasing order and logic of the natural world. What musical properties did Plato observe, which reflect a "pleasing order and logic"? Can you think of elements incorporated in music presently, such as pitch, pitch orderings, rhythms, techniques, and chance elements, that are perhaps less pleasing to some? If so, what music would you select to illustrate those particular qualities? What might these properties and your musical examples reveal about our contemporary world?

III. The philosophers Plato and Aristotle wrote about the power of music and its role in ordering a just and moderate society. What current music do you believe may affect your behavior, and what about that music moves your conduct? What other potentials do you think music may hold?

Name _____

Class/Section _____ Date _____

CHAPTER 2
The Elements of Music

🎵 Terms

Match each term with the correct definition below by placing the correct letter in the space provided.

a. Noise
b. Musical Tone
c. Frequency
d. Pitch
e. Amplitude
f. Dynamics
g. Timbre or Tone Color

h. Duration
i. Rhythm
j. Soprano
k. Alto
l. Tenor
m. Bass
n. Pianissimo

o. Piano
p. Mezzo Piano
q. Mezzo Forte
r. Forte
s. Fortissimo
t. Decrescendo
u. Crescendo

1. _____ the lowest female vocal range, also called contralto; an instrument that performs in a range similar to this voice type

2. _____ the lowest male voice register; an instrument that performs in a range similar to this voice type

3. _____ to gradually get louder

4. _____ to gradually get softer

5. _____ sound producing a series of regular, predictable pulsations, which possess four basic definitive characteristics; frequency, volume, timbre, and duration

6. _____ any sound producing a series of irregular, unpredictable pulsations, causing diffusion in aural clarity

7. _____ the furthest distance a vibrating object travels; the degree of displacement

8. _____ the loudness or softness of sound; or the volume of a musical passage

9. _____ the speed or rate of vibrations occurring in a sound-producing body

10. _____ the highness or lowness of musical sound

11. _____ the length of time a particular sound or silence lasts

12. _____ in general terms, the organization of sound and silence through time

13. _____ the sonorous quality of tone of a particular voice or instrument, or a group of voices or instruments; dependent on the amount and proportion of overtones present

14. _____ the highest female voice register; an instrument that performs in a range similar to this voice type

15. _____ the highest natural adult male singing voice; an instrument that performs in a range similar this voice type

16. _____ a dynamic directive that means "loud"

17. _____ a dynamic directive that means "very soft"

18. _____ a dynamic directive that means "moderately soft"

19. _____ a dynamic directive that means "moderately loud"

20. _____ a dynamic directive that means "very loud"

21. _____ a dynamic directive that means "soft"

𝄢 Fill in the Blank

22. The orchestral double-reed woodwind instrument that shares much of the flute's pitch range, but because of a wider, longer cone-shaped body possesses a powerful low-pitch register and is thereby heard as an alto instrument at various times, is the _____.

23. The pitch range of wind instruments is governed by the length and width of its _____.

24. The orchestral brass instrument that utilizes the widest and longest conical tubing, with a bell pointing upward, is the modern orchestral _____.

25. The _____ has the shortest and most narrow tubing of the orchestral brass instruments, and is the soprano member of this family.

26. The oldest known keyboard instrument, dating back two thousand years, which has many sets of pipes controlled from several keyboards, including a pedal keyboard, is the _____.

27. The orchestral string instrument, which has a large pitch range that covers soprano and alto registers is the _____.

28. Various sets of pipes on a pipe organ are brought into play by pulling knobs called _____.

29. Depressing keys on the keyboard of a _____ sets into motion felt hammers that reach up to strike tuned strings.

30. Depressing keys on the keyboard of a _____ brings into play little quills that rise to pluck tuned strings.

31. Among the oldest instruments, dating as far back as 3000 B.C., which requires the performer to pluck or strum its strings, one for each pitch, is the _____.

32. The soprano member of the orchestral woodwind family that relies on the performer's ability to direct air in and across an open tone-hole at one end of its long, narrow, cylindrical tube is the

_____.

33. Singers' voice types, in addition to pitch range, are often further classified with regard to character and _____, the third basic property of musical sound.

34. The orchestral percussion instrument that consists of a large copper drum and parchment skin is the

_____.

Questions for Discussion or Essay

I. Music appears to be an intrinsic part of all human experience as it is easily encountered almost everywhere we go. After taking a moment to consider the ways you encounter it daily, and then imagining what the quality of life would be without it, discuss how music affects your daily life.

II. Although no previous musical knowledge is required for an introductory course, each student has undoubtedly experienced by now a variety of musical venues and may even embrace specific musical preferences. What type or types of music do you find most interesting or exciting? Why? Do you believe that extensive or even limited exposure to certain types of music might play a part in how a person perceives music? How so?

CHAPTER 3
Pitch Designations and Relationships in Music

𝄢 Terms

Match each term with the correct definition below by placing the correct letter in the space provided.

a. Interval
b. Chromatic
c. Enharmonic
d. Octave
e. Scale
f. Whole Step or Whole Tone
g. Diatonic Scales

h. Major Scales
i. Minor Scales
j. Church Modes
k. Dorian
l. Phrygian
m. Lydian
n. Mixolydian

o. Locrian
p. Pentatonic Scale
q. Whole-Tone Scale
r. Octatonic Scale
s. Atonal
t. "Blue" Note

1. _____ having no tonal center, avoiding any sense of tonality

2. _____ an altered pitch usually slightly beneath the one expected

3. _____ the set of twelve pitches represented by all the white and black keys on the piano within one octave

4. _____ the distance between two pitches

5. _____ pitch orderings that date back to ancient Greece, represented by several pitch orientations of the diatonic scales with D, E, F, G, and B, as tonics, instead of the tonal scales represented by C and A

6. _____ the natural scales consisting of five whole steps and two half steps, produced by the white keys on the piano

7. _____ a church mode represented by the white keys from D to D on the piano

8. _____ a church mode represented by the white keys from B to B on the piano

9. _____ a church mode represented by the white keys from F to F on the piano

10. _____ a church mode represented by the white keys from G to G on the piano

11. _____ a church mode represented by the white keys from E to E on the piano

12. _____ a collection of pitches chosen for a particular piece

13. _____ an interval of eight notes, represented by the white keys on the piano, where a pitch is perceived as being duplicated

14. _____ a diatonic scale represented by the white keys of the piano keyboard, oriented around C as the tonic; characterized by half-step intervals between the third and fourth tones and seventh and eighth tones, with whole tones between all other consecutive steps

15. _____ a diatonic scale represented by the white keys of the piano keyboard, oriented around A as the tonic; the third and, usually, sixth and seventh notes are lower by a half-step than those in the major scale, giving it a less bright quality

16. _____ an interval that is equal to two half-steps or semitones

17. _____ a six-tone scale consisting exclusively of whole steps

18. _____ an ancient five-tone scale, represented in the relation of the black keys of the piano

19. _____ an eight-tone scale alternating between whole and half-steps

20. _____ used to describe notes spelled differently, but having the same pitch

𝄢 Fill in the Blank

21. In the contemporary Western European system, there are _____ basic pitches spaced an equal distance apart when presented in their respective ascending or descending order, without repeating any of them at the octave.

22. When pitches are heard ascending or descending by half-steps, we say they are moving _____.

23. In speaking or singing, men's voices will usually be one or two _____ lower than women's voices.

24. The chromatic scale consists exclusively of _____ steps.

25. Among the most widely used, the diatonic scales consist of _____ whole steps and two half-steps.

26. Under a system called "solfege," the central note or tonic in a major scale is commonly referred to as _____.

27. All of the diatonic scales may be produced, and thereby represented, by the _____ keys on the piano.

28. When the tonic pitch is A in a diatonic scale, it is referred to as a _____ scale.

29. Diatonic pitch orderings that can be traced back to the music of ancient Greece, which were later used in early Christian church and secular music and are still utilized in a good deal of contemporary music, are often referred to as _____.

30. When a musical work lacks any sense of a tonal center it is referred to as _____.

Questions for Discussion or Essay

I. In addition to exploring 479,001,600 possible arrangements of the basic twelve tones, some Western composers make use of the fact that our ears are capable of detecting, within a wide array of perceptible sounds, an infinite number of pitches within the range of an octave and no longer rely solely on a restricted number of fixed pitches chosen from this sound continuum, by means of tuning systems, to make music. Do you believe that the contemporary Western European tuning system of twelve basic pitches spaced an equal distance apart is sufficient for all music making? Why or why not? Do you think alternative-tuning systems might play an even larger role in Western European contemporary music? If so, what would be the advantages? If not, what would be the disadvantages? (To answer these questions, you might weigh a composer's choice of pitches for a particular piece against the effects of light and color perceived and thus expressed by way of color values selected by a visual artist.)

II. Many of you have already experienced synthesized sounds, as well as post-tonal alternatives, incorporated into the soundtracks of many films, pop songs, and the like, reflecting possibilities seemingly only limited by the human imagination. What advantages or disadvantages do you perceive in each of the above-mentioned approaches to music making? What other alternative techniques have you experienced? What was the context? What advantages or disadvantages to their use did you perceive?

CHAPTER 4
Musical Notation

Terms

Match each term with the correct definition below by placing the correct letter in the space provided.

a. Staff
b. Ledger Lines
c. Treble Clef or G Clef
d. Bass Clef or F Clef
e. Flat
f. Sharp
g. Whole Note
h. Half Note
i. Quarter Note
j. Eighth Note

k. Sixteenth Note
l. Rests
m. Dotted Rhythms
n. Time Signature
o. Bar Lines
p. Measures
q. Simple Meters
r. Common Time
s. Compound Meters
t. Tempo

u. Largo
v. Lento
w. Adagio
x. Andante
y. Andantino
z. Moderato
aa. Allegretto
bb. Allegro
cc. Vivace
dd. Prestissimo

1. _____ a unit of meter, consisting of a principal strong beat and one or more weaker ones

2. _____ vertical lines through the staff used to show measures

3. _____ a sign used to indicate meter, represented by a fraction in which the upper figure shows beats per measure and the lower figure shows the time value of each beat

4. _____ the pace at which rhythmical units progress

5. _____ metric groupings in *duple* (2/2, 2/4, 2/8), *triple* (3/2, 3/4, 3/8), and *quadruple* (4/2, 4/4, 4/8) time

6. _____ simple meters, multiplied by three: *compound duple meter* (6/2, 6/4, 6/8), *compound triple meter* (9/4, 9/8), and *compound quadruple meter* (12/4, 12/8, 12/16)

7. _____ a musical meter with four beats to the measure, and the quarter note equals the beat; often referred to as four-four time

8. _____ the five lines and four spaces used to indicate graphically the relative highness or lowness of pitch

9. _____ a clef that puts G above middle C on the second line of the staff, used for the higher pitch frequencies

10. _____ a clef indicating that a note on the fourth line of the staff represents F, an interval of a fifth below middle C, used for the lower pitch frequencies

11. _____ short extra lines added above and below the staff used to accommodate a few higher or lower pitches

12. _____ a symbol indicating that the note to which it is fixed is to be played one half-step above the specified note

13. _____ a symbol indicating that the note to which it is fixed is to be played one half-step below the specified note

14. _____ the longest note commonly used in modern music

15. _____ a note that rhythmically divides the quarter note by two

16. _____ a note that is half the length of the whole note

17. _____ a note that rhythmically divides the half note by two

18. _____ a note that rhythmically divides the eighth note by two

19. _____ short silences in music; the notational symbols indicating silences

20. _____ an amalgamated rhythm produced when a dotted note is followed by a shorter note, or vice versa

21. _____ a tempo indication that means very slow, broad

22. _____ a tempo indication that means very quick

23. _____ a tempo indication that literally means very vivacious, very fast

24. _____ a tempo indication that means slow

25. _____ a tempo indication that means slow, leisurely

26. _____ a tempo indication that means less lively than *allegro*, moderately fast

27. _____ a tempo indication that literally means lively, fast

28. _____ a tempo indication that means moderate

29. _____ a tempo indication that means slow to moderate walking pace

30. _____ a tempo indication that means a little faster that *andante*

Fill in the Blank

31. To avoid excessive use of ledger lines, a pianist usually reads _____ clef when playing lower pitch registers, from middle C down.

32. A _____ sign is used when a pitch is to be lowered by a half-step.

33. The note found in the center of the piano keyboard, separating treble pitches from bass pitches, is called middle _____.

34. A staff is made up of _____ horizontal lines and a resulting four spaces.

35. A _____ is placed at the beginning of a staff to show a point of reference for pitch.

36. Short silences are called _____ in music.

37. The term _____ refers to the rate of speed of the basic pulse of the music.

38. A dot to the right of a note or rest increases its duration by _____.

39. Compound meters are simple meters multiplied by _____.

40. The upper number of a musical time signature tells how many _____ there are in a measure.

41. The _____ number in a musical time signature indicates the unit of measure, establishing the pulse of a piece.

42. A _____ sign is used when a pitch is to be raised by a half-step.

43. The _____ clef is used for relatively high pitches, such as those usually played by a pianist's right hand.

44. The basic beat will be grouped into recurring patterns or time units, separated by _____ lines, relating respective measures of time.

45. The strongest beat in a metric unit will fall on the _____ beat.

🎼 Questions for Discussion or Essay

I. Not all aspects of music making can be notated; the most obvious trait is perhaps musical expression. What other aspects of music making appear to defy notation, aspects that rely solely on the performer?

II. Notational systems remain in constant flux, and many contemporary additions to Western European musical notation are necessitated by the desire to incorporate additional pitches, rhythms, colors, and techniques. Some notational examples, although they are not yet standardized, are found on pages 35–36 of your textbook. Can you think of any other performance characteristics that may be notated? What symbols would you devise to clearly indicate those aspects?

CHAPTER 5
The Structures of Music

Terms

Match each term with the correct definition below by placing the correct letter in the space provided.

a. Melody	p. Harmony	ee. Fugue Subject
b. Phrase	q. Chord	ff. Exposition
c. Climax	r. Consonance	gg. Answer
d. Cadence	s. Dissonance or Discord	hh. Countersubject
e. Theme	t. Style	ii. Episode
f. Augmentation	u. Form	jj. Pedal Point
g. Diminution	v. Theme and Variations	kk. Chain Suspension
h. Fragmentation	w. Introduction	ll. Retrograde
i. Motive	x. Coda	mm. Inversion
j. Texture	y. Ritornello Form	nn. Stretto
k. Monophony	z. Ritornello	oo. Sonata Form
l. Polyphony	aa. Concerto	pp. Development
m. Imitative Polyphony	bb. Concerto Grosso	qq. Recapitulation
n. Non-Imitative Polyphony	cc. Cadenza	rr. Bridge
o. Homophony	dd. Fugue	ss. Cadence theme
		tt. Rondo Form

1. _____ the repetition of a theme using notes that are lengthened in value, thus slowing it down

2. _____ the process of reducing a theme to fragments

3. _____ the repetition of a theme using notes that are shortened in value, thus speeding it up

4. _____ means "topic"; a principal or basic subject of a piece of music

5. _____ a succession of single pitches going somewhere with an appeal to the senses, heard as a recognizable whole

6. _____ a short musical idea consisting of at least two notes, forming the basis for development in a piece of music

7. _____ a sequence of notes that form a unit in music, each leading sensibly to the next

8. _____ a term used to describe the various sounds and melodic lines taking place concurrently in a piece of music

9. _____ the most exciting or important moment, or the point a melody or entire piece strove for

10. _____ notes that give pause or end, to a passage, or work, with some degree of conclusiveness

11. _____ three or more notes played or sung simultaneously to harmonize and embellish a melody

12. _____ a texture describing two or more melodies played or sung simultaneously

13. _____ a texture describing one unaccompanied melody

14. _____ a musical texture that describes two or more simultaneous melodic lines that are quite different

15. _____ a musical texture describing two or more simultaneous melodic lines using the same or quite similar melodies, but with staggered entrances

16. _____ a combination of musical notes that usually form chords; the vertical aspect of music

17. _____ a musical texture that describes only one melody of real interest presented with other sounds used to harmoniously support it

18. _____ the recognized way in which the formal elements of a work have been handled so as to provide the whole with expressive effect

19. _____ intervals or chords, or any other musical sounds that sound relatively tense, harsh, biting, or unstable

20. _____ intervals or chords, or any other musical sound combinations that sound free of tension or discord

21. _____ associated with musical interactions that produce a sense of shape and structure

22. _____ a polyphonic composition for an established number of voices, built on a single principal theme called the subject, since all of the parts are based on the same material

23. _____ a relatively joyful, simple form; the fundamental principle is the unvaried repetition of a main theme, commonly called a "tune"

24. _____ means "large concerto"; it is an instrumental work that requires many solo instrumentalists rather than just one, and an orchestra

25. _____ a form that is sometimes referred to as "first-movement form" or "sonata-allegro form"

26. _____ means "to contend," it is an instrumental work for soloist or a group of soloists and an orchestra

27. _____ a form that consists of a theme followed by a series of variations on it

28. _____ linear material that serves as the basis for all parts of a fugue; it is relatively brief, but distinctively bold, usually consisting of relatively few pitches and clear rhythms for easy recognition

29. _____ the practice of manipulating themes and motives in various ways; it also refers to the section of sonata form in which themes from the exposition undergo this process

30. _____ means "tail"; a musical section placed at the end of a piece or movement that does not represent part of a described form such as theme and variations form

31. _____ an improvised solo within a larger work otherwise notated, such as a concerto

32. _____ a musical section added to the beginning of a piece or movement that does not represent part of the described form such as theme and variations form

33. _____ a transitional passage; in sonata form, a modulating passage that moves from the tonic key to a second key, connecting to main themes

34. _____ closing material that is usually less distinct than other themes in a piece; sometimes consisting of only descending scales or chords

35. _____ the second voice of a fugue, which enters in a second key as contrast

36. _____ a distinctive polyphonic line that recurrently accompanies the subject of a fugue in another voice

37. _____ when harmonic resolutions are prolonged by repeatedly holding over one or more pitches from a preceding chord into the next, which would have otherwise resolved the prior harmonic tension

38. _____ the first section of a fugue or a sonata-form movement

39. _____ when one voice in a fugue overlaps with another; entering before another has finished

40. _____ the last section of a sonata-form movement in which all the thematic material of the exposition returns in its original order; however, all of the themes now appear in the tonic

41. _____ reading or playing a musical line or series backward

42. _____ as a term that most often pertains to an organist's foot ("pedal"), which manipulates a pedal keyboard, it is used for holding a single bass note while other voices progress with a succession of changing harmonies against it

43. _____ diversionary music in a fugue that often appears to wander, since all the melodic lines start to move freely and the tonality constantly modulates

44. _____ reading or playing a musical line or series upside down; reversing all its upward intervals downward and vice versa

45. _____ a Baroque form that utilizes the recurrences of a ritornello theme

46. _____ the orchestral material that is introduced at the beginning of a movement of a work such as a concerto, which always returns, usually in fragments and in different keys throughout

𝄢 Fill in the Blank

47. Sonata form is sometimes referred to as "sonata-allegro form" because it has so frequently been used for the _____ movements of sonatas, symphonies, string quartets, and so on.

48. The emotional impact of the development section in sonata form is achieved by musically developing any or all thematic material introduced in the _____.

49. Each linear line in a fugue is referred to as a _____.

50. In a concerto, an improvised solo passage that is usually based on previous material is called a _____.

51. The fundamental principle in _____ form is the unvaried repetition of a main theme, commonly called the tune, because of its typical playful character.

52. In sonata form, the psychological impact of the recapitulation is the resolution of conflict and a return to _____.

𝄢 Questions for Discussion or Essay

I. Beethoven's *Fifth Symphony* as well as the movies *Jaws* and *Psycho* were used as examples in the text-book, to reflect the enormous power a musical motive could possess. Did you recognize any of these examples? If so, were you previously aware of any motivic use in the music? What advantages do you experience in noticing motives in film music? Can you think of any other musical scores that make use of motives?

II. Ritornello form fundamentally encourages the listener to anticipate the orchestral returns of the ritornello, although they are treated differently, as recognized phrases between contrasting material provided by a group of soloists, building to an emotional climax three-quarters through a movement. Please describe the ways orchestral returns may build climatic tension. Why do you think the emotional climax in this form usually arrives three-quarters of the way through the movement? Can you think of any other pieces that use this form or one that is quite similar?

Name _____

Class/Section _____ Date _____

CHAPTER 6
Ancient Greece

Recorded Anthology

The Epitaph of Seikilos

Fill in the Blank

1. The study of music in the ancient world has largely been left up to _____ rather than musicians.

2. Instruments made from the bones of giant mammals and dating to approximately 200,000 B.C. were discovered among the artifacts associated with humans living during the _____ Age.

3. Perhaps the oldest written music from the West dates from roughly 2300 B.C. and the ancient civilization of Ugarit, located in what is now the nation of _____.

4. Found in Mesopotamia are clay tablets that mention garments specially made for professional _____.

5. Among the oldest examples of musical notation appearing in papyrus manuscripts that date from approximately 130 B.C., are two Delphic hymns to _____.

6. Like the sung tragedies of ancient Greece, modern _____ are sung from beginning to end.

7. A *Skolion* is a kind of Greek _____ song.

8. *The Epitaph of Seikilos* is a song that was carved into the _____ of a Greek who once lived on what is now the coast of Turkey.

9. The notation for *The Epitaph of Seikilos* is known as Greek "_____" notation.

10. Like all the existing examples of Greek musical notation, *The Epitaph of Seikilos* is _____, comprising only a melody.

11. Iconographic evidence often shows singers accompanied by instruments, and in the recorded anthology accompanying this text we hear a plucked string instrument called a _____.

12. For many ancient Greeks, Pythagoras included, _____ were crucial to understanding all things material and spiritual.

13. _____ argued that music of a certain character and emphasizing certain pitches could channel the powers associated with the planets and result in music specially suited to sway the audience in predictable and valuable ways.

14. Plato believed that music was perfectly suited to discipline the _____ of the young.

𝄢 Questions for Discussion or Essay

I. Though they are not mutually exclusive, the struggle between intellect and emotion is one of the most significant, ongoing struggles in the history of Western arts. For the Greeks, the battlefield of this struggle was often musical. What favored appeals to the intellect or emotions constitute your choices of music? Why? Can you find elements of both in your musical selections? What are they?

II. Plato's idealism, like so much idealism, turned to nostalgia for an order in music he hoped would never change, writing in his *Republic* "A change to a new type of music is something to beware of as a hazard to all our fortunes." Do you believe that Western departures from the modes used in ancient Greece and the freewheeling use of dissonance in many contemporary pieces have disturbed the most fundamental political and social foundations of modern society as Plato argued would happen? Please give specific examples as to why you believe Plato was correct or to why you think he was not. Are you idealistic about conserving particular music, or do you champion new avenues for musical expression? Why?

Name _____

Class/Section _____ Date _____

CHAPTER 7
The Middle Ages (c. 476–1452)

Recorded Anthology

Match each composition with its composer by placing the correct letter in the corresponding space provided to the right (note: two composers are anonymous).

a. Anonymous
b. Guillaume Dufay
c. Pérotin
d. Bernart de Ventadorn
e. Philippe de Vitry

1. "Alleluia" from the *Mass for Christmas Day*
2. "Ysaias Cecinit"
3. "Can vei la lauzeta mover"
4. *Garrit Gallus/In Nova Fert*
5. "Istampita Palamento"
6. "Nuper Rosarem Flores"

1. _____
2. _____
3. _____
4. _____
5. _____
6. _____

Terms

Match each term with the correct definition below by placing the correct letter in the space provided.

a. Mass Proper
b. Mass Ordinary
c. Matins
d. Vespers
e. Church Modes
f. Monophony
g. Polyphony
h. Sequences
i. Tropes
j. Conductus
k. Rhythmic Modes

l. Troubadours
m. Strophic Form
n. Motet
o. *Roman de Fauvel*
p. Isorhythm
q. "Color"
r. Talea
s. Psaltery
t. Lute
u. Recorder
v. Vielle

1. _____ pitch orderings that date back to ancient Greece, represented by several pitch orientations of the diatonic scales with D, E, F, G, and B, as tonics, instead of the tonal scales represented by C and A

2. _____ a system of notation at Notre Dame during the 13th century that allowed for interesting rhythmic variety

3. _____ the 14th century technique of constructing a piece with a voice that comprises a borrowed, repeating melodic line (the color) and a repeated rhythmic pattern (the talea)

4. _____ a vocal composition with parts for different voices; early secular ones consisted of secular material on top of pre-existing sacred material, usually based on fragments of a Gregorian chant

5. _____ a texture describing one unaccompanied melody

6. _____ in the medieval Christian church, a phrase or text interpolated into the established repertory of the Mass

7. _____ in the medieval Christian church, sequential passages added to the chant repertory

8. _____ compositions frequently used at Notre Dame in the 13th century to accompany religious processions; in English we still use the word "conduct" to indicate moving from place to place

9. _____ a musical texture that occurs when two or more musical lines of more or less equal importance unfold simultaneously

10. _____ a musical form where the same melody is sung with each new verse of poetry

11. _____ poet-composers who flourished primarily in southern France during the twelfth and early thirteenth centuries, their primary poetical concern was the articulation and celebration of the idea of courtly love

12. _____ texts that are present in every Mass celebration

13. _____ those texts that changed from day to day in the celebration of the Mass, dictated by a church calendar that was built around three annual cycles

14. _____ one of the most celebrated books of the Middle Ages, a collection of poems that satirizes the foibles of the day

15. _____ canonical hours celebrated just prior to sunrise

16. _____ canonical hours celebrated at sunset

17. _____ the repeated cycles of notes usually performed by a musical instrument rather than a singer, because there is so little text, in the third voice of an isorhythmic piece

18. _____ the recurrent rhythmic pattern in an isorhythmic piece

19. _____ an end-blown fipple flute still in use today

20. _____ a bowed string instrument vaguely like the modern violin

21. _____ a string instrument which is similar to the modern zither

22. _____ a plucked string instrument slightly similar to the modern guitar

𝄢 Fill in the Blank

23. Perhaps the most influential person to hold the office of Pope, Pope _____ sought to codify Christian practices so that Christians throughout Europe would worship in the same manner.

24. Housing a large number of scholars, the cathedral of _____ in Paris was the home to the most robust activity in terms of additive composition, that is, the layering of new material onto old.

25. The _____ system was a political division of territory into units that was based on a system of "vassalage," modeled on the church's system of vassalage.

26. The Middle Ages represents the roughly 1000 years from 476 A.D., when the last Roman Emperor was overthrown, to _____, when Constantinople, the capital of the eastern half of the Roman Empire, fell to the Turks.

27. Medieval Christianity emphasized mystery and _____ over the more rationalized approaches to Christianity advanced after the advent of the Protestant Reformation during the early 1500s.

28. The text for all Gregorian Chant is in _____, the official language of the medieval church and also the official language of the sciences, law, scholarship, and much literature of the Middle Ages.

29. Gregorian Chant utilizes a _____ rhythmic system that suited the church's beliefs and practices perfectly, discouraging foot tapping or any other sense of sensual pleasure, which would have been viewed as blasphemous.

30. The particular Church Mode used for "Alleluia" from the *Mass for Christmas Day* and Bernart de Ventadorn's "Can vei la lauzeta mover" is the _____ mode.

31. The medieval composer, poet, and the Bishop of Meaux, who wrote mainly secular music, which included important contributions to the celebrated book *Roman de Fauvel* was _____.

32. Fauvel is a _____ with magical powers to grant wishes when anyone combs or curries his coat.

🎼 Questions for Discussion or Essay

I. The medieval sense that humankind's temporary realm of existence was relatively unimportant is reflected in much of the music of the early Middle Ages, which was composed by men and women who made no attempt to sign their work and enjoy the admiration of future generations. Pride, one of the Seven Deadly Sins articulated during the Middle Ages, was a deterrent for these devout believers. Discuss how the word "pride" is often used presently. What do you derive from its meaning? What role do you think pride may play in contemporary music making?

II. How does the medieval practice of using an already existing piece of music and adding new material to it reflect a specific time and place, and the medieval imagination? What advantages do you imagine Philippe de Vitry saw in stacking three highly independent musical lines, which incorporate similar but different texts on top of one another, and using the most sophisticated structural technique of the day (isorhythms) in his motet *Garrit Gallus/In Nova Fert*? What are some modern examples of the same processes at work? How may this type of structure be advantageous today? How might this modern process mirror a specific time and place, and contemporary imagination?

Name _____

Class/Section _____ Date _____

CHAPTER 8
The Renaissance (1452–1600)

🎼 Recorded Anthology

Match each composition with its composer by placing the correct letter in the corresponding space provided to the right.

a. Claudio Monteverdi
b. Palestrina
c. Josquin des Prez
d. Giaches de Wert

1. *Missa Hercules dux Ferrarie, Agnus Dei*
2. *Pope Marcellus Mass, Agnus Dei*
3. *Vezzosi augelli*
4. *Cruda Amarilli*

1. _____
2. _____
3. _____
4. _____

🎼 Terms

Match each term with the correct definition below by placing the correct letter in the space provided.

a. Humanism
b. Text Setting
c. Declamation
d. Points of Imitation
e. Council of Trent
f. Movement
g. Neighbor Tone

h. Passing Tone
i. Madrigal
j. Text Painting
k. Melisma
l. Florentine Camerata
m. Opera
n. Monody

1. _____ music specially designed to accommodate the words by paying special attention to every syllable stress and dramatic implication

2. _____ an organization of intellectual and artistic talent devoted to the revival of the ancient Greek practice of singing their tragic dramas

3. _____ the belief in the power and importance of human beings and their achievements

4. _____ a conference of Catholic leaders, both secular and sacred, at the Italian city of Trent that was organized by Pope Paul III to examine and criticize time-honored doctrines of the church

5. _____ when a dissonance such as a second is resolved by still further stepwise motion away from the original pitch

6. _____ when a dissonance such as a second is resolved by motion back to the previous note

7. _____ dramatic vocal music for solo voice with instrumental accompaniment

8. _____ a dramatic work of art presented in music; thought of initially as a string of musical works performed one right after another which, taken together, tell a complete story

9. _____ a polyphonic composition for unaccompanied voices; ideally they feature responsive settings of elegant, secular poetry

10. _____ the musical illustration of the text

11. _____ when words are set in music by incorporating rhythms and melodies that approximate normal speech patterns

12. _____ term used for a large, self-contained section within a larger work, such as an opera

13. _____ a decorative phrase or passage in vocal music, in which one syllable of text is sung to a melodic sequence of several notes

14. _____ the technique of writing a melody in one vocal part, and then having another voice enter in the next measure singing the same notes the previous voice had just sung, but unlike a full-fledged round it would not continue with strict imitation for long

Fill in the Blank

15. The first use of the word "Renaissance" to describe the period in European history from roughly 1452 until 1600 belongs to the _____ -century French historian Jules Michelet.

16. Today, many scholars refer to the period from 1452–1600 as "early _____," providing the advantage of documenting that certain medieval priorities had given way to something new, without condemning the Middle Ages and its cultural priorities.

17. Most historians agree that the main intellectual and philosophical challenge to the medieval imagination's preference for faith in the Renaissance period was _____, the belief in the power and importance of human beings and their achievements.

18. The Renaissance represents those times when Western society relied on humankind's own power to make sense of an explicable world through the powers of _____.

19. "Renaissance" is a French word meaning "_____."

20. The principal figure in the Catholic response to Luther's objections about opaque and incomprehensible music designed for the Mass, and whose compositional style was stimulated by the action of the Council of Trent, was _____.

21. The composer _____ would often select a popular tune (sometimes even a bawdy tune) and use it as the basis for each part of the Mass.

22. Monteverdi justified his use of _____ and its improper preparation under the rules of Zarlino in his madrigal *Cruda Amarilli* by pointing out that the words take precedence over the tones.

♩ Questions for Discussion or Essay

I. The spirit of humanism fueled the Renaissance, impacting the way composers approached music. What are some of the techniques these composers used to connect their music to humanism? Could you say that the Middle Ages, which placed a premium on faith and uncertainty, was any less humanistic than the Renaissance with its reliance on human achievement? How would you characterize today's music?

II. Monteverdi shattered the rules for careful dissonance treatment in his madrigal *Cruda Amarilli*, arguing that the words take precedence over the musical tones; when the text speaks of cruelty, the music should capture the pathos of the speaker through passionate dissonance. Did Monteverdi's use of dissonance to accentuate the emotions of the poem convey stronger emotions to you, than if he had otherwise judiciously followed the rules laid out earlier in the century by Zarlino? Do you believe that dissonance, in and of itself, could produce a cruel or painful sensation, or do you think that such value judgments and extravagant claims of certain sensations being cruel or painful are a learned response? What ways might dissonance be utilized today?

III. The history of the madrigal reflects a move towards professionalism: earlier practitioners of the madrigal, working between roughly 1530 and 1550, saw the form as primarily a diversion for the wealthy, a form intended for amateur use, as the music generally lacked difficult musical features; the second phase of madrigal composition, roughly 1550–1580, saw more difficult and intricate text and tone relationships; in the final phase of the madrigal, practiced from 1580 to the end of the century, composers strove to marry their music to the least change of meaning or tone in the poetry, and used extravagant techniques toward that end, requiring trained musicians. Today most people do not make their own music. What does the late Renaissance dependence on professionals tell us has changed since ancient times (remember, Plato pitied the person who relied on professional musicians to entertain them)? Are these changes for the better? What does our modern dependence on others for musical entertainment tell us about our society?

Name _____

Class/Section _____ Date _____

CHAPTER 9
The Baroque Period (1600–1750)

Recorded Anthology

Match each composition with its composer by placing the correct letter in the corresponding space provided to the right (note: some composers will need to be listed more than once).

a. Johann Sebastian Bach
b. George Frideric Handel
c. Jean-Baptiste Lully
d. Claudio Monteverdi
e. Barbara Strozzi
f. Antonio Vivaldi

1. *L. Orfeo*, "In fiorito prato" through "Tuse morta"   1. _____
2. *Lagrime mie*   2. _____
3. *The Four Seasons, la primavera*, first movement   3. _____
4. *Armide*, "Enfin il est en ma puissance"   4. _____
5. *Rinaldo*, "Cara sposa"   5. _____
6. *Messiah*, "There were shepherds"   6. _____
7. *Messiah*, "Halleluia" Chorus   7. _____
8. Brandenburg Concerto No. 2   8. _____
9. *Saint Matthew Passion*, "Ach Golgatha"   9. _____
10. *The Art of the Fugue*, Contrapunctus III   10. _____

Terms

Match each term with the correct definition below by placing the correct letter in the space provided.

a. Baroque
b. The Doctrine of Affections
c. Opera
d. Monody
e. Basso Continuo Group
f. The Concertato Principle
g. Vocal Cantata
h. Recitative
i. Aria

j. Arioso
k. Castrato
l. Oratorio
m. Concerto
n. Ritornello Form
o. Program Music
p. Concerto Grosso
q. Fortspinnung
r. Fugue

s. Fugue Subject
t. Countersubject
u. Exposition
v. Episode
w. Movement
x. Trillo
y. Passagio

11. _____ a vocal number sung solo or as a duet with orchestra in a work such as an opera, oratorio, or cantata

12. _____ a cross between the declamatory style of recitative and the lyric style called "aria"

13. _____ a male singer who was castrated before puberty in order to maintain a soprano

14. _____ continuous ("*continuo*") bass ("*basso*"), performed by low-pitched instruments such as the cello, bass, or bassoon on the bass part, with a keyboard instrument such as an organ or harpsichord, the performer's left hand reinforcing the bass line, while the right hand continuously plays chords being outlined, note-by-note, in the bass; the instrumental group that performs this part

15. _____ comes from the Portuguese language; *"barroco"* refers to a pearl of irregular shape

16. _____ calls for composers to combine diverse musical forces, such as choruses combined with an ensemble of brasses in the same piece, toward a common purpose, as opposed to one basic timbre, most often human voices

17. _____ is one aesthetic ideal that draws on the notion that the arts should move the emotions, so the artist must select a desired affect, an emotional state that his or her work will achieve in the viewer or listener, which evokes a single, unadulterated emotional state

18. _____ means "to contend," it is an instrumental work for soloist or group of soloists and orchestra

19. _____ means "large concerto"; it is an instrumental work that requires many solo instrumentalists rather than just one, and orchestra

20. _____ a distinctive polyphonic line that recurrently accompanies the subject of a fugue in another voice

21. _____ the first section of a fugue (or a sonata-form movement)

22. _____ diversionary music in a fugue that often appears to wander, since all the melodic lines start to move freely and the tonality constantly modulates

23. _____ means "forward spinning"; a motivic technique that makes the melody of a work seem almost endless; just as one instrument's melodic phrase is coming to an end, another instrument enters with a fresh melodic idea

24. _____ a polyphonic composition for an established number of voices, built on a single principal theme called the subject, since all parts are based on the same material

25. _____ the single principal theme of a fugue, as all parts will be based on the same linear material

26. _____ dramatic vocal music for solo voice with instrumental accompaniment

27. _____ term used for a large, self-contained section within a larger work, such as a concerto

28. _____ a dramatic work of art presented in music; thought of initially as a string of musical works performed one right after another which, taken together, tell a complete story

29. _____ a large-scale composition for soloists, chorus, and orchestra that tells a story, much like opera; but unlike opera, these stories are usually religious and meant to be performed without costumes or stage movement

30. _____ a sizable work for small orchestra, chorus, and vocal soloists, either sacred or secular

31. _____ an ornament comprising quick runs up and down scales, often heard during the singing of a Baroque opera

32. _____ when the same note is sung over and over in rapid succession, a Baroque style ornament

33. _____ instrumental music associated with an extra-musical idea or story

34. _____ speech-like singing

35. _____ a Baroque form that utilizes the recurrences of a *ritornello* theme; the orchestral material that is introduced at the beginning of a movement of a work such as a concerto, which always returns, usually in fragments and in different keys throughout

𝄢 Fill in the Blank

36. In Greek mythology Orfeo (or Orpheus) was the demi-god of music, and had the power to charm listeners by singing and playing the _____.

37. In Barbara Strozzi's *Lagrime mie*, it is safe to assume that the vocal part was originally written for a _____, a voice which possessed the virtue of a boy's high register coupled to a full-grown man's vocal power.

38. Antonio Vivaldi received a post as instructor of music at an orphanage run by the church in Venice, which served only the abandoned or orphaned _____ of Venice.

39. Vivaldi's formal plan for the first movement of his Spring Concerto (*la primavera*) is _____.

40. Appearing simultaneously with the widespread adoption of capitalism as an available means of making money, the _____ can be seen as the genre that brought money and fame to outstanding instrumentalists.

41. Unlike Italian opera, French *tragedie-lyrique* (lyric tragedy) was full of visual spectacle, borrowing from two great French traditions, spoken tragedy and _____.

42. The action of Jean-Baptiste Lully's *Armide* takes place during the _____.

43. The titular character Armide is an Islamic _____ who has been campaigning against the crusading Renaud.

44. George Frideric Handel's *Messiah* is one his most famous _____, a genre meant to be performed without costumes or stage movement.

45. Johann Sebastian Bach wrote _____ Brandenburg Concertos, named for the margrave of Brandenburg, to whom Bach sent all copies.

46. Bach musically set the text *"Ach Golgatha"* from the gospel according to _____.

𝄢 Questions for Discussion or Essay

I. Although the story of Handel's opera *Rinaldo* is almost identical to Lully's *Armide*—Rinaldo (the Italian equivalent of the French hero, Renaud, from *Armide*) is participating in the First Crusade and meets up with the Islamic sorceress, Armide—there are striking national distinctions. Discuss the differences between Handel's Italian operatic treatment and Lully's French *tragedie-lyrique* (lyric tragedy).

II. Bach composed a series of fugues called *The Art of the Fugue* to leave as a monument to posterity on the craft of writing in this fashion, fearing that the subtleties and values of this technique might be lost. How might a piece that would mainly serve the purposes of study, rather than performance, differ from a work composed for a specific performance venue?

CHAPTER 10
The Classical Period (1750–1825)

𝄢 Recorded Anthology

Match each composition with its composer by placing the correct letter in the corresponding space provided to the right (note: two composers will need to be listed twice).

a. Ludwig Van Beethoven
b. Christoph Willibald Gluck
c. Franz Joseph Haydn
d. Giovanni Battista Pergolesi
e. Wolfgang Amadeus Mozart

1. "La serva padrona"
2. *Orfeo ed Euridice*
3. Symphony No. 56
4. Piano Concerto No. 17 in G, K. 453
5. "Madamina" from *Don Giovanni*
6. Symphony No. 3, in E♭ Major, op. 55
7. Piano Sonata No. 31, in A♭ Major, op. 110

1. _____
2. _____
3. _____
4. _____
5. _____
6. _____
7. _____

𝄢 Terms

Match each term with the correct definition below by placing the correct letter in the space provided.

a. Gallant Style
b. Intermezzo
c. Da capo aria
d. Classical
e. Symphony
f. Sonata Form
g. Exposition
h. Development
i. Recapitulation
j. Introduction
k. Coda
l. Bridge
m. Cadence Theme
n. Theme and Variations
o. Binary Form
p. Hammerstrokes
q. Hemiola
r. Sonata
s. Fermata
t. Arpeggio

8. _____ relating to or belonging to the ancient Greeks and Romans or their culture; a term that implies a model of excellence to be emulated

9. _____ a chord that is played one note after another in succession, either ascending or descending, rather than simultaneously

10. _____ closing material that is usually less distinct than other themes in a piece; sometimes consisting of only descending scales or chords

11. _____ a transitional passage; in sonata form, a modulating passage that moves from the tonic key to a second key, connecting to main themes

12. _____ means "tail"; a musical section placed at the end of a piece or movement that does not represent part of a described form such as theme and variations form

13. _____ an aria in ABA form, which results from the opening A section sung da capo at the end

14. _____ the practice of manipulating themes and motives in various ways; it also refers to the section of sonata form in which themes from the exposition undergo this process

15. _____ the first section of a fugue or a sonata-form movement

16. _____ a cessation of counting; to "hold" a note or chord longer than the time value indicated

17. _____ a detached emotional musical style favored in the Enlightenment that looks outward to society and is anxious to please; as compared to dramatic styles of the Baroque period that are puffed up with their own pathos and emotion

18. _____ loud chords that typically began an overture; used to give the audience fair warning that the opera was about to start

19. _____ a relatively short piece of music that is performed between longer movements of an extended composition such as an opera

20. _____ a musical section added to the beginning of a piece or movement that does not represent part of the described form such as sonata form

21. _____ the last section of a sonata-form movement in which all the thematic material of the exposition returns in its original order; however, all of the themes now appear in the tonic

22. _____ a multi-movement work for one or more instruments; at least one movement is in sonata form

23. _____ a genre usually exemplifying the following characteristics: instruments only, multi-movements, lofty musical ambitions, and an abstract subject matter; some exceptions include singers in symphonies, a single long movement, intentionally trivial in nature, or the incorporation of concrete story lines

24. _____ a form that is sometimes referred to as "first-movement form" or "sonata-allegro form"

25. _____ a two-part musical form with different sections indicated: **AB**

26. _____ a form that consists of a theme followed by a series of variations on it

27. _____ rhythms that work at cross purposes with the prevailing meter; a rhythmic alternation of two notes in the place of three, or three notes in the place of two

𝄢 Fill in the Blank

28. "La serva padrona" is an _____ from Pergolesi's most celebrated intermezzo.

29. _____ is the person who defined "taste" as follows "Genius creates, but taste selects: and a too abundant genius is often in want of a severe censor to prevent it from abusing its valuable riches."

30. The project of Enlightenment in the West is configured around the questioning of powerful institutions on _____ grounds.

31. Gluck hoped to create operas in which the structure of the opera was determined by the needs of the _____.

32. The earliest symphonies were written by Italian composers as overtures for their _____.

33. The first movement of Haydn's Symphony No. 56 is in _____ form.

34. Mozart uses _____ form for the third movement of his Piano Concerto No. 17 in G, K. 453.

35. "Madamina" from Mozart's opera, *Don Giovanni*, is the famous "catalogue _____."

36. Beethoven's middle period (1802–1816) is often referred to as his "_____" period.

37. Beethoven expressed to his brothers in a letter now known as "The Heiligenstadt Testament," that he often thought of ending his wretched life. He wrote, "Only _____ held me back."

38. Beethoven had initially dedicated his Symphony No. 3 to _____, a person whom he earlier admired, before violently scribbling over the name with an ink pen and rededicating it to an anonymous hero; the symphony now known by the Italian word for heroic, *"eroica."*

39. The first movement of Beethoven's *Eroica* symphony opens with two loud _____.

40. The instrument that Beethoven played and for which he wrote multiple sonatas is the _____.

Questions for Discussion or Essay

I. Now that you have read this chapter on the Classical Period and the previous chapter on the Baroque, you are aware that Monteverdi's opera *Orfeo* and Gluck's opera *Orfeo ed Euridice* use the same legend of Orfeo (or Orpheus) and Euridice from Greek mythology. Please discuss in as much detail as you can specific characteristics of each work. How is each composition structured? How does each composition reflect the time period in which it was composed? What was each composer trying to achieve? Do you believe one style relates the legend more successfully that the other? If so, which one and why? If not, please explain how the legend might be successfully explored using divergent musical styles.

II. Jean-Jacques Rousseau favored the pleasing and simple style of the "gallant style," arguing that music is the product of genius, but genius only triumphs when it submits to the norms of taste, which existed as the common property of all persons of wisdom and breeding. He defined "taste" in his *Dictionary of Music* (1767) as follows: "Genius creates, but taste selects: and a too abundant genius is often in want of a severe censor to prevent it from abusing its valuable riches. One can do great things without taste, but it is taste that makes them interesting." Such claims lead to fundamental questions: What function if any does art have in society? Should an artist be open to allowing their genius to be tempered by others, or should an artist utilize their genius to challenge audiences by shedding new light or perspective on particular issues or subjects? How might unbridled genius serve the greater good? In an American age of individualism and information, does our society have a responsibility to encourage individuals who pioneer new forms of expression in music?

III. Beethoven's middle period (1802–1816), often referred to by scholars as his "heroic" period, is markedly distinct from the prevailing tastes of the day. What is the difference between Rousseau's conception of taste and the way Beethoven conceived it in his Symphony No. 3, *(Eroica)*? What events had changed since Rousseau's time to explain a transformation of taste?

CHAPTER 11
Romanticism (1820–1900)

Recorded Anthology

Match each composition with its composer by placing the correct letter in the corresponding space provided to the right (note: one composer will need to be listed twice).

a. Vincenzo Bellini
b. Hector Berlioz
c. Frédéric Chopin
d. Nikolai Rimsky-Korsakov
e. Franz Schubert
f. Clara Schumann
g. Robert Schumann
h. Richard Wagner

1. "Gretchen am Spinnrade"
2. *Norma*
3. Nocturne in F-sharp
4. *Symphonie Fantastique*
5. *Fantasiestucke*
6. *Waldesgesprach*
7. Fugitive Piece No. 1
8. *Das Ring des Nibelung, Die Walküre*
9. *Farewell and Departure of the Tsar*

1. _____
2. _____
3. _____
4. _____
5. _____
6. _____
7. _____
8. _____
9. _____

Terms

Match each term with the correct definition below by placing the correct letter in the space provided.

a. Art Song or Lied
b. Strophic
c. Ostinato
d. Ternary Form
e. Nocturne
f. Schubertiads
g. Volkstummlichkeit

h. Grandiose
i. Program Music
j. Idée Fixe
k. Dies Irae
l. Bel Canto Style
m. Two-Tempo Aria
n. Banda

o. Cabaleta
p. Music Drama
q. Leitmotifs
r. Gesamtkunstwerk
s. Linear Chromatic Harmony

10. _____ Italian for "beautiful singing," a term that sums up the principal goal of Italian opera composers and audiences during the Romantic period

11. _____ "Day of wrath"; one of the gravest Gregorian chants frequently heard in Catholic requiem masses throughout France, and was used by Berlioz in his *Symphonie Fantastique*

12. _____ "total artwork"; a term used by Wagner as a way of expressing his ideal of fusing all the arts at their highest perfection so that the whole of this fusion would be greater than the sum of its parts

13. _____ a "fixed idea" or obsession; a term Berlioz uses for a recurring theme, which carries programmatic meaning, in all of the movements of his *Symphonie Fantastique*

14. _____ refers to the instrumentalists placed on stage in Italian opera

15. _____ the musical setting of a poem, usually performed by solo voice and piano, in which the performers are expected to contribute significantly to the artistic effect of the poetry

16. _____ guiding motives that were used as a principal means of connecting the music to the drama in Wagner's music dramas

17. _____ a term Wagner used for his distinctive type of opera

18. _____ a short musical phrase or melody that is repeated over and over, usually at the same pitch

19. _____ instrumental music associated with an extra-musical idea or story

20. _____ an aria that is based on an important tempo change partway through; it opens with a "scena," a section of recitative that advances the action, moves to a "tempo primo," or first tempo section, which then moves to another called the "tempo di mezzo," or middle tempo, and concludes with a rousing "cabaleta," a section that caps off the form, giving the "two-tempo aria" three tempi, which makes the label a misnomer

21. _____ a German word meaning "folk voice-ness," or in musical terms, when thoroughly professionalized music strives to sound like folk song

22. _____ musical evenings that were paid for by the wealthy, in which Schubert and a few friends would play piano works, art songs, and chamber music at an aristocratic home

23. _____ when all stanzas of the text in a song are sung to the same music

24. _____ a genre that centers on the evocation of moods and feelings associated with the night, which has no preconceived formal plan associated with it

25. _____ a conception Wagner embraced, the dramas are lengthy, the orchestra is huge, and the singers must have extremely powerful voices and stamina

26. _____ a rousing section that caps off the "two-tempo aria" through the return of the tonic

27. _____ polyphonic lines that create harmony with pitches outside the tonic scale, often moving chromatically

28. _____ a three-part musical form in which the last section repeats the first and the middle section differs, indicated: **ABA**

𝄢 Fill in the Blank

29. Schubert's song "Gretchen am Spinnrade" presents a text from Goethe's epic drama _____.

30. The term _____ refers to a musical phrase that is repeated persistently.

31. Giuditta Pasta was a (voice type)_____ for whom Vincenzo Bellini wrote his operas, and whom he eventually married.

32. Gioacchino Rossini's formal plan for the aria was based on an important tempo change part way through the aria. Today scholars call Rossini's approach the _____.

33. The "two-tempo aria" ends with a rousing _____, a section that caps off the form through the return of the tonic.

34. Chopin specialized in composing for the _____, his instrument.

35. The label "two-tempo aria" is a little misleading since it has _____ tempi.

36. A group of instrumentalists who appear on stage in an opera is called a _____.

37. The genre that was developed by the Irishman, John Field, and centers on the evocation of moods and feelings associated with the night is the _____.

38. Berlioz's *Symphonie Fantastique* is an example of _____ music, instrumental music that associates itself with some extra-musical idea.

39. The transformation of the idealized beloved Irish Shakespearean actress, Harriet Smithson, in Berlioz's *Symphonie Fantastique*, into a melody was a brilliant stroke, a _____ theme, as it were, that he encounters and hears everywhere.

40. The *Dies irae* ("Day of Wrath") is a _____ from the requiem Mass.

41. Robert Schumann's *Fantasiestucke* is a piece for solo _____, the favorite solo instrument of the Romantic period.

42. In Robert Schumann's *Waldesgesprach* ("Forest Conversation") the singer must take on two implied roles, that of the supernatural being, the Lorelei, and that of a _____ who meets up with her in the forest at night.

43. Though Clara Schumann's Fugitive Piece No. 1 uses a wonderful application of small-scale variation; the formal plan of the piece is simple _____ form.

44. Richard Wagner's *Das Ring des Nibelung, Die Walküre* (the second music drama) concludes with Wotan punishing his beloved daughter, Brünnhilde. Wagner creates for Wotan's farewell an individual _____ for each of these central elements: sleep, farewell, love, magic fire, binding agreement, Loge (the fire elemental) and Siegfried (the as yet unborn hero).

45. Rimsky-Korsakov's *Farewell and Departure of the Tsar* features _____ (the country) nationalism; quoting folk songs, borrowing idiomatic dance rhythms, and using distinctly national themes (such as events, literature, or fairy tales).

Questions for Discussion or Essay

I. E.T.A. Hoffmann applied the word Romanticism to music by describing Mozart as a Romantic, especially in his opera *Don Giovanni*, as Hoffmann was taken with the singularity of Mozart's genius and his willingness to defy convention in expressing powerful emotional states. Now that you have read both the Classical and Romantic period chapters and listened to the music, describe in as much detail as you can how Mozart may have expressed such compelling emotional states in his opera. What elements would you consider to show Classical sensibility and what elements would you consider to be Romantic? Why?

II. How is the subject of "love" romanticized in the opera *Norma*? Do you believe Bellini's bel canto style and formulas for composing operas helped to support such Romantic themes? How so?

III. Wagner's music was termed "music of the future" by the second editor of Robert Schumann's journal the *Neue Zeitschrift für Musik*, Franz Brendel. Although many of Wagner's ideas and compositional techniques have certainly paved the way for twentieth century composers, both his music and philosophy seem to capture just about every aspect of nineteenth century Romanticism. Describe Wagner's philosophy with respect to his "music dramas," your musical example *Das Ring des Nibelung, Die Walküre* in particular, and how his philosophy as well as his music reflect Romantic sensibilities.

CHAPTER 12
Concert Music 1900–1945

𝄢 Recorded Anthology

Match each composition with its composer by placing the correct letter in the corresponding space provided to the right.

a. Claude Debussy	1. "Nacht" from *Pierrot Lunaire*	1. _____
b. Charles Ives	2. Gnossienne No. 1	2. _____
c. Erik Satie	3. "The Dialogue of the Wind and Waves," from *La Mer*	3. _____
d. Arnold Schoenberg	4. *The Rite of Spring*	4. _____
e. Igor Stravinsky	5. *Charlie Rutledge*	5. _____
f. Germaine Tailleferre	6. *Waltz of Telegrams*	6. _____
g. Anton Weben	7. Concerto, op. 24	7. _____

𝄢 Terms

Match each term with the correct definition below by placing the correct letter in the space provided.

a. Modernism	h. Transposition	o. Fauve Style
b. Expressionism	i. Sprechstimme	p. Primitivism
c. Atonality	j. Impressionism	q. Ostinato
d. Unifying Motive	k. Pentatonic Scale	r. Neo-Classicism
e. Retrograde	l. Whole-Tone Scale	s. Twelve-Tone Method,
f. Inversion	m. Chromatic Scale	Twelve-Tone Technique or Serialism
g. Retrograde Inversion	n. Octatonic Scale	t. Tone Row

8. _____ a movement in music that calls for the creation of a more perfect modernism through the combination of modern musical traits with orderly principles borrowed from music's past or from popular styles

9. _____ a short-lived "wild beast" style in the early part of the twentieth century that experimented with distorting images and incorporating motifs from primitive art

10. _____ an early twentieth-century movement expressing revolutionary ideas and styles as a reaction to traditional forms

11. _____ a twentieth-century artistic movement that seeks the expression of pure emotional states liberated from all repression, exploring dark, previously hidden emotions or pure and ecstatic emotional states once considered taboo

12. _____ a compositional method in which the composer creates a row of all twelve pitches of the chromatic scale to provide the motivic information that will hold the piece together, while assuring atonality

13. _____ a late nineteenth and early twentieth-century French artistic movement; in music, a style concerned with keeping certainty at bay; characterized by blurring formal, rhythmic, and tonal boundaries to express scenes or emotions

14. _____ having no tonal center, avoiding any sense of tonality

15. _____ the set of twelve pitches represented by all the white and black keys on the piano within one octave

16. _____ to move an entire piece, or a section of a work, or a scale, or a twelve-tone row up or down in pitch, preserving all of the intervallic relationships within the unit

17. _____ reading or playing a musical line or series backward

18. _____ reading or playing a musical line or series upside down and backward

19. _____ reading or playing a musical line or series upside down; reversing all its upward intervals downward and vice versa

20. _____ refers to Schoenberg's theory that motives, and not tonal centers, hold pieces together

21. _____ refects an early twentieth-century interest in preliterate culture, utilizing a deliberate evocation of primordial power through insistent rhythms, percussive sounds, and sexual energy

22. _____ an ancient five-tone scale, represented in the relation of the black keys of the piano

23. _____ a six-tone scale consisting exclusively of whole steps

24. _____ an eight-tone scale alternating between whole and half-steps

25. _____ "speaking voice"; the singer does not sing in the usual sense, but declaims the text by speaking on pitches, creating a spoken melody

26. _____ the ordering of the twelve chromatic pitches used in serialism

27. _____ refers to a musical phrase that is repeated persistently

Fill in the Blank

28. The early twentieth-century movement that pressed Romantic fervor to its ultimate conclusion by exploring an inner world of reality as described by Sigmund Freud was _____.

29. In Albert Giraud's expressionist poems, _____ is the eternal figure of the sad clown.

30. Erik Satie's Gnossienne No. 1 is written for solo (the instrument) _____.

31. In Erik Satie's Gnossienne No. 1, the exotic opening-melody in f-minor is accompanied by a harmony that is so simple, that in fact, it uses only _____ chords.

32. The composer _____ expressed "Pleasure is the law," which gets to the heart of the matter in his music.

33. Impressionism is often associated with the composer _____.

34. After the Franco-Prussian War, France and Russia sought to resist Germany's growing military and economic strength by forming a _____.

35. Diaghilev formed the *Ballets Russes* and moved it to _____ (the city).

36. Stravinsky's ballet *The Rite of Spring* tells a story about a tumultuous moment for a tribe of prehistoric _____.

37. *The Rite of Spring* begins with a solo _____ playing the opening theme.

38. The American composer _____ was born in Connecticut, the son of a municipal bandleader.

39. In the song "Charlie Rutledge," a setting of words by D.J. O'Malley, "Charlie" is an American _____.

40. The waltz by Germaine Tailleferre in our recorded anthology represents Parisian _____ (the movement).

41. "The twelve-tone method" was a system devised by the composer _____.

42. Anton Webern dedicated his Concerto, op. 24 to Schoenberg on his birthday, and uses both the twelve-tone method and Schoenberg's favorite sonority, a _____-note grouping; the same sonority previously used by Schoenberg in the piece "Nacht" from *Pierrot Lunaire*.

𝄢 Questions for Discussion or Essay

I. Many composers during the previous century actively sought to distance themselves from Romanticism. Why so? Can you find aspects of Romanticism still operating in the pieces in this chapter? What are they?

II. The desire for newness and innovation in contemporary music, in order to distance it from historical music, came to be known as modernism, now commonly called "the avant-garde." Which pieces in this chapter reflect modernism? Does the term "modernism" accurately reflect those works presently? If so, how? If not, why?

III. Neo-classicism is a movement in music that calls for the creation of a more perfect modernism through the combination of modern musical traits with orderly principles borrowed from music's past or from popular styles. With this, how does Germaine Tailleferre's *Waltz of Telegrams* reflect Parisian neo-classicism? What aspects of the piece reflect modern musical traits, and what aspects are borrowed principles? How does Tailleferre's music reflect collaboration with the poet Jean Cocteau, who organized this ballet?

IV.   Rousseau, who argued that genius must be censored by taste, would not have agreed with the modernists, which sought to shed all pretense of trying to please everybody. For the modernist Diaghilev, that always meant offending more than a few people along the way, reassuring Stravinsky over the riot at the premiere of his ballet, *The Rite of Spring* (1913), saying, "Success is easy; scandal requires genius!" Is there anything about *The Rite of Spring* that warranted the audience to riot? Would anyone riot over the piece today? Do you believe scandal requires genius? How so? Do you believe everyone during Rousseau's time had always been pleased by performances that met his standards? Should a composer always feel obligated to fulfill Rousseau's criteria? If so, why? If not, how may the function of music in society change from Rousseau's view of it? What functions, if any, do to think art serves today?

Name _____

Class/Section _____ Date _____

CHAPTER 13
Concert Music (1945–Present)

Recorded Anthology

Match each composition with its composer by placing the correct letter in the corresponding space provided to the right (note: one composer will need to be listed twice).

a. Milton Babbit
b. Pierre Boulez
c. John Cage
d. George Crumb
e. Annea Lockwood
f. Edgard Varèse

1. Le Marteau sans maître
2. *Poème electronique*
3. *Philomel*
4. *Music of Changes*
5. "Glass Rod Vibrating," from *Glass Concerts*
6. "Turning Gong" and "Mini Mobile," from *Glass Concerts*
7. *Black Angels*, Scenes 6 and 7 from Part II

1. _____
2. _____
3. _____
4. _____
5. _____
6. _____
7. _____

Terms

Match each term with the correct definition below by placing the correct letter in the space provided.

a. Avant-Garde
b. Integral Serialism
c. Surrealism
d. Alto Flute
e. *Musique concrete*
f. Synthesizer

g. Indeterminacy
h. Minimalism
i. Quotation
j. Trill
k. Obbligato
l. Glissando

8. _____ an artistic method of organization that sought to remove personal desires and ambitions from art by letting some system of choosing other than one's own desires dictate the outcome

9. _____ a kind of eclectic quotation of past material and styles which does not necessitate adopting any particular overall style, in fact, it intervenes against adopting a single style

10. _____ a larger version of the usual flute capable of producing lower pitches and a darker tone

11. _____ relating to mathematical integrals or integration; in music, a comparably closed system where all parameters of a piece (timbre, dynamics, rhythms, pitches) are either regulated by individual rows, as the European integral serialists had done, or by one row common to all parameters, reflected in many compositions by Milton Babbitt, a leading advocate of integral serialism in America

12. _____ a musical ornament produced by the rapid alternation between two adjacent pitches

13. _____ a term taken from French military terminology; in the arts it refers to the new generations of modernists whose work is innovative, experimental, or unconventional

14. _____ an instrument that produces musical sounds through purely electrical means

15. _____ a twentieth-century French artistic movement that believed that the world of the subconscious as experienced in dreams constituted something more important than waking reality, which they mistrusted, and achieved their ends by casting together violent and irrational juxtapositions

16. _____ compositions comprising recorded acoustic sounds

17. _____ a twentieth-century style of composition emphasizing the use of a small amount of musical material either repeated or elongated over a vast period of time

18. _____ the addition of a short contrapuntal melody to another main melody at indicated places

19. _____ a string technique that asks the performer to slide up or down on a string

Fill in the Blank

20. After the Second World War, a second important split in the art of music took place between _____ music and classical music.

21. The competition between the capitalist West and the communist East after the Second World War, which led the two sides to confront one another in almost every field of endeavor, became know as the _____ War.

22. After World War Two, _____ stepped in as a major patron of avant-garde music.

23. The composer who believed in such slogans as "Don't try to change the world, you'll only make matters worse," and consequently radical methods of organizing pieces in order to free his compositions of his desires was _____.

24. The _____ music festivals included concerts, discussions, and courses aimed at helping young composers from throughout Europe in their effort to locate a style suitable for the aftermath of World War Two.

25. Although the split between avant-garde music and classical music has some relationship to class, it might be more centrally concerned with _____.

26. Edgard Varèse wrote *Poème electronique* for the Philips Corporation's pavilion at the _____ World's Fair.

27. George Crumb's *Black Angels* was inspired in part by the _____ War, to serve as a post-holocaust parable on the desolation, hopelessness, and disillusionment all too often experienced in our troubled contemporary world.

28. One of the more solemn musical quotations from earlier works utilized by George Crumb in *Black Angels* is *Death and the Maiden* by the nineteenth-century composer _____.

Questions for Discussion or Essay

I. Adoption by the mainstream is not a goal of the avant-garde. What were some of the reasons for pursuing the extremes of radical organization undertaken after World War Two? What contemporary qualities in our society do you see contributing against the general public coming to know this music? Do you think this condition of relative obscurity for this repertoire reflects a particular problem or an advantage? Why do you believe avant-garde composers continue pursuing music that is not intended for the mainstream?

II. How does Annea Lockwood, the radical young composer who studied music in New Zealand, use John Cage's work as a useful point of departure for her *Glass Concerts*? Did either composer completely succeed in divorcing personal intentions and desires in bringing their respective works into existence? Why would composers pursue such a potentially impossible mission?

CHAPTER 14
Ragtime and Jazz

Recorded Anthology

Match each composition with its composer.

a. Duke Ellington
b. Lilian Hardin
c. Scott Joplin
d. Thelonious Monk
e. Cecil Taylor

1. "Maple Leaf Rag"
2. "Hotter Than That"
3. "Ko-Ko"
4. *Misterioso*
5. "Air," from *The World of Cecil Taylor*

1. _____
2. _____
3. _____
4. _____
5. _____

Terms

Match each term with the correct definition below by placing the correct letter in the space provided.

a. Ragtime
b. Jazz
c. Classical
d. Popular
e. Traditional

f. Scat
g. Big Band
h. Improvisation
i. Be-Bop
j. "A Warrior Culture"

k. Free Jazz
l. "Out" Jazz
m. New Orleans Style
n. Latin Jazz
o. Fusion

6. _____ a liberated and combative form of jazz that presented listeners with the loosest of compositions, allowing for wildly intuitive solos

7. _____ refers to music that is primarily configured as a disposable commodity, having the following sorts of objective elements: some strong commercial appeal, rapid changes in audience taste quickly accommodated in the music itself, and a social function that seldom caters to silent or immobile contemplation of the music itself so much as the making of a total scene involving dancing, fashion, and other forms of socializing

8. _____ an American classical music genre that flows out of many traditions including ragtime, the blues, the improvised music of African Americans in the decades following emancipation, spirituals, and the various musics of West Africa as remembered by the men and women who came to this country from there

9. _____ refers to music that emphasizes the composer, is usually written down, intends to appeal to posterity, and, while often functional, can also be treated as art for art's sake

10. _____ a genre of American music that originated around the turn of the twentieth century that is closely associated with one central figure in its history, Scott Joplin; usually notated and published for piano, it benefited from the participation and contributions of several composers with excellent classical training, and came to the attention of jazz musicians who used them

as a framework for their own improvisatory performances; it is characterized by distinctive syncopated right-hand rhythms against a regularly accented left-hand beat

11. _____ a rather poetic reference to be-bop, as be-bop musicians took on characteristics of warriors priding themselves on their achievements and holding lesser players in contempt

12. _____ a style of jazz representing a fusion of jazz and rock 'n' roll

13. _____ describes all that music that is born of anonymous authors and has been passed down by word of mouth; the creators are not so much trying to establish a position for themselves as widely recognized musicians, but rather they are integrating their music-making into a social fabric, with much of folk music having little commercial value because it is readily available and easily accessible both for performers and listeners.

14. _____ the creative process of performing without preparation or set notation to follow

15. _____ refers to a wordless vocal improvisation

16. _____ a style of jazz that stems from the activity of musicians in Latin America where local dance traditions like the samba in Brazil inform players and serve as the framework for improvisatory performances

17. _____ a form of jazz meant for connoisseurs who wanted to compare the intricate details of complex solos played at blistering tempos and within a super-sophisticated harmonic language

18. _____ a style of jazz that originated in New Orleans where most ensembles presented a fairly undifferentiated polyphonic texture of group improvisation from the beginning of a piece to the end

19. _____ another reference to free jazz, since it, like a good deal of avant-garde concert music, was not intended for a mass audience and it afforded its practitioners an outsider's art that never came inside

20. _____ an ensemble of fairly large scale including several trumpets, trombones, saxophones, clarinets, a pianist, a drummer, and a bass player

Fill in the Blank

21. Scott Joplin earned additional income from playing the piano in the evening at the _____ Club, a club that saw the flourishing of "the sporting life."

22. The form of Joplin's famous "Maple Leaf Rag" is basically _____, although there are two repeated segments within each larger part of the form.

23. Scott Joplin's ragtime piano music characteristically follows an unusual tonal plan emphasizing the _____, or sub-dominant, instead of the more traditional fifth, or dominant, as his polar key.

24. Sometimes Louis Armstrong sang his solos rather than playing them on trumpet, a wordless vocal improvisational version referred to as "_____."

25. In Jazz, each rendition of the song is called a _____.

26. New developments in New York City were taking shape at the Roseland, where Fletcher Henderson and his orchestra were attracting large crowds, which led to a type of jazz ensemble that came to be known as a _____.

27. Louis Armstrong's instrument was the _____; an instrument received as a gift, it became his ticket out of a life of poverty and neglect.

28. Thelonious Monk participated in "a warrior culture," performing a style of jazz called _____.

29. The jazz movement which took its name from a recording released in 1965 by saxophonist Ornette Coleman and led to one that would create still a more perfect "outsider art," is called _____ jazz.

30. Following a long tradition that exists in musical studies, dating back at least to the work of Bruno Nettl in the 1960's that differentiates between three types of music, the accurate musical classification for "jazz" is _____.

🎼 Questions for Discussion or Essay

I. Scott Joplin insisted that his intentions be honored when performing his music; he wrote and published a short tract on ragtime called *School of Ragtime*, and made piano rolls for use on player pianos in an effort to demonstrate the proper way to play his music. Joplin's efforts ultimately failed as too many people wanted to play his works, which allowed the market to win out over his original intentions. What did Joplin seek to encapsulate in his music and in performance? Can you think of other ways, both good and bad, the market shapes music and musicians presently?

II. Public settings such as nightclubs, where the audience may be enjoying drinks and conversation, provide the most common venue for jazz performance. These venues are not so different from the salons of past centuries, as the formality of the nineteenth-century concert, where lights are turned down on an audience seated in fixed chairs that face the stage and who are required to refrain from food, drink, and conversation, is the exception rather than the rule in Western concert music. Please discuss the advantages or disadvantages of creating art in both a formal and informal setting. What do you think would be the ideal setting for musical genres such as opera, chamber music, or jazz? Why? Citing specific examples, how may a particular venue affect the style of music created? If a musical composition was intended for an ideal setting, does the function or meaning of the piece change if it is taken from its original context?

CHAPTER 15
Postmodernism

Recorded Anthology

Match each composition with its composer.

a. Robert Ashley   1. *Atalanta: Acts of God*   1. _____
b. John Zorn   2. *Cobra*   2. _____

Terms

Match each term with the correct definition below by placing the correct letter in the space provided.

a. Postmodernism   c. Resistance
b. Modernism   d. Reaction

3. _____ a sensibility that is characterized by an active distancing of present practices, both artistic and social, from the practices of a past that no longer gets to dictate the terms of its meaning or value

4. _____ an artistic movement where form follows function, and is associated with the concepts of purpose, closed forms, design, hierarchy, ends oriented, permanence, and linear progress

5. _____ a sensibility that accepts the generic procedures of the past, and turns these procedures into the service of a game of forms

6. _____ a twentieth-century movement that moves away from the ideal of form follows function; all the past's artifacts, no matter how respectfully they were once viewed, can be used in playful combinations without respect for original context or function; it is associated with the concepts of play, open forms, chance, anarchy, means oriented, impermanence, and random access

Fill in the Blank

7. Exemplified by the skyscraper in the field of architecture, where clean lines present glass towers of the utmost utility, maximizing usable space by the stacking of floor upon floor, is the _____ ideal of form following function.

8. The *Piazza d'Italia* in New Orleans provides a good illustration of postmodern architecture by the architect _____, who is widely seen a leader in the movement.

9. Characteristic procedures used by postmodernist must be one of two sensibilities: _____ or reaction.

10. Robert Ashley's piece *Atalanta: Acts of God* is an example of a postmodern _____ (the genre) that was written for television.

11. The First Lady of the United States from 1969 to 1974, who traveled to China with her husband Richard Nixon, was _____ Nixon.

12. John Adams most closely resembles Charles Moore in respect to his postmodernist sensibility of _____, drawing upon past styles and depriving them of their original function.

13. In Greek legend, _____ could run faster than any man, and was so strong and virtuous that, when her father sought an appropriate husband for her, many obstacles were placed in the prospective husband's path.

14. In Robert Ashley's *Atalanta: Acts of God*, _____ abduct three men: the surrealist painter Max Ernst, storyteller Willard Reynolds, and pianist Bud Powell.

15. To perform John Zorn's *Cobra*, one needs a goodly number of fine musicians and a leader, who has _____ that contain symbols that tell the ensemble what to do.

16. John Zorn claims that his shortened attention span is due to watching _____ for hours and hours during his youth, and consequently his music changes drastically from moment to moment in only a minute or two.

𝄢 Questions for Discussion or Essay

I. Many college-campus activities can certainly serve as contemporary examples in exploring postmodern sensibilities. As many readers of this book may be college students, please describe the function of the university you attend, and relate any mounting game of forms that appear to be replacing that function? Do you find yourself actively participating in any activities that reflect the postmodern characteristics?

II. How does John Zorn's composition *Cobra* reflect postmodern sensibilities? What aspects of this work might reflect skepticism about traditions of Western logic?

Name _____

Class/Section _____   Date _____

(Please staple the program or ticket stub to the back of this report.)

First Concert Report

Introduction

A. What was the event? _____

B. Where did the event take place?_____

C. What was the date and time of the event?_____

D. What was your general reaction to the concert environment?

_____

_____

_____

_____

Body

E. What was the *first work performed* (the title and the composer)?

_____

_____

1. Specific observations of the work, both aural and visual (the genre, historical style, form, movements, fundamental elements of rhythm, tempo, dynamics, mode, texture, timbre, and so forth).

_____

_____

_____

_____

_____

_____

_____

_____

2. What is your overall reaction? For example: What do you think the composer sought to accomplish? Do you think he or she succeeded? Why or why not? Do you think the performers were successful in communicating the piece? Why or why not?

_____

_____

_____

_____

_____

_____

F.　What was the *last work performed* (the title and the composer)?

_____

_____

1. Specific observations of the work, both aural and visual (the genre, historical style, form, movements, fundamental elements of rhythm, tempo, dynamics, mode, texture, timbre, and so forth).

_____

_____

_____

_____

_____

_____

_____

_____

2. What is your overall reaction? For example: What do you think the composer sought to accomplish? Do you think he or she succeeded? Why or why not? Do you think the performers were successful in communicating the piece? Why or why not?

_____

_____

_____

_____

_____

_____

G. Please select a work you found of particular interest, other than those already mentioned (the title and the composer).

_____

_____

1. Specific observations of the work, both aural and visual (the genre, historical style, form, movements, fundamental elements of rhythm, tempo, dynamics, mode, texture, timbre, and so forth).

_____

_____

_____

_____

_____

_____

_____

_____

2. What is your overall reaction? For example: What do you think the composer sought to accomplish? Do you think he or she succeeded? Why or why not? Do you think the performers were successful in communicating the piece? Why or why not?

_____

_____

_____

_____

_____

_____

𝄢 Conclusion

H. Please give some overall comments about this concert experience.

_____

_____

_____

_____

(Please staple the program or ticket stub to the back of this report.)

| *Second Concert Report*

Introduction

A. What was the event? _____

B. Where did the event take place? _____

C. What was the date and time of the event? _____

D. What was your general reaction to the concert environment?

_____

_____

_____

_____

Body

E. What was the *first work performed* (the title and the composer)?

_____

_____

1. Specific observations of the work, both aural and visual (the genre, historical style, form, movements, fundamental elements of rhythm, tempo, dynamics, mode, texture, timbre, and so forth).

_____

_____

_____

_____

_____

_____

_____

_____

2. What is your overall reaction? For example: What do you think the composer sought to accomplish? Do you think he or she succeeded? Why or why not? Do you think the performers were successful in communicating the piece? Why or why not?

_____

_____

_____

_____

_____

_____

F. What was the _last work performed_ (the title and the composer)?

_____

_____

1. Specific observations of the work, both aural and visual (the genre, historical style, form, movements, fundamental elements of rhythm, tempo, dynamics, mode, texture, timbre, and so forth).

_____

_____

_____

_____

_____

_____

_____

2. What is your overall reaction? For example: What do you think the composer sought to accomplish? Do you think he or she succeeded? Why or why not? Do you think the performers were successful in communicating the piece? Why or why not?

_____

_____

_____

_____

_____

_____

G. Please select a work you found of particular interest, other than those already mentioned (the title and the composer).

_____

_____

1. Specific observations of the work, both aural and visual (the genre, historical style, form, movements, fundamental elements of rhythm, tempo, dynamics, mode, texture, timbre, and so forth).

_____

_____

_____

_____

_____

_____

_____

_____

2. What is your overall reaction? For example: What do you think the composer sought to accomplish? Do you think he or she succeeded? Why or why not? Do you think the performers were successful in communicating the piece? Why or why not?

_____

_____

_____

_____

_____

_____

_____

Conclusion

H. Please give some overall comments about this concert experience.

_____

_____

_____

_____

Name _____

Class/Section _____ Date _____

(Please staple the program or ticket stub to the back of this report.)

Third Concert Report

Introduction

A. What was the event? _____

B. Where did the event take place?_____

C. What was the date and time of the event?_____

D. What was your general reaction to the concert environment?

_____

_____

_____

_____

Body

E. What was the *first work performed* (the title and the composer)?

_____

_____

  1. Specific observations of the work, both aural and visual (the genre, historical style, form, movements, fundamental elements of rhythm, tempo, dynamics, mode, texture, timbre, and so forth).

_____

_____

_____

_____

_____

_____

_____

_____

2. What is your overall reaction? For example: What do you think the composer sought to accomplish? Do you think he or she succeeded? Why or why not? Do you think the performers were successful in communicating the piece? Why or why not?

_____

_____

_____

_____

_____

_____

F. What was the *last work performed* (the title and the composer)?

_____

_____

1. Specific observations of the work, both aural and visual (the genre, historical style, form, movements, fundamental elements of rhythm, tempo, dynamics, mode, texture, timbre, and so forth).

_____

_____

_____

_____

_____

_____

_____

2. What is your overall reaction? For example: What do you think the composer sought to accomplish? Do you think he or she succeeded? Why or why not? Do you think the performers were successful in communicating the piece? Why or why not?

_____

_____

_____

_____

_____

_____

G. Please select a work you found of particular interest, other than those already mentioned (the title and the composer).

_____

_____

1. Specific observations of the work, both aural and visual (the genre, historical style, form, movements, fundamental elements of rhythm, tempo, dynamics, mode, texture, timbre, and so forth).

_____

_____

_____

_____

_____

_____

_____

_____

_____

2. What is your overall reaction? For example: What do you think the composer sought to accomplish? Do you think he or she succeeded? Why or why not? Do you think the performers were successful in communicating the piece? Why or why not?

_____

_____

_____

_____

_____

_____

_____

Conclusion

H. Please give some overall comments about this concert experience.

_____

_____

_____

_____

_____